SPRING FUN

DOT-TO-DOT ACTIVITY BOOK

Written and Illustrated by
Barbara Soloff-Levy

Watermill Press

Spring is here. Raindrops are falling.
The grass is getting greener. The rain
is making everything grow, especially
this _____ .

This bulb was planted in the fall. Now it is starting to grow and bloom into a beautiful _____.

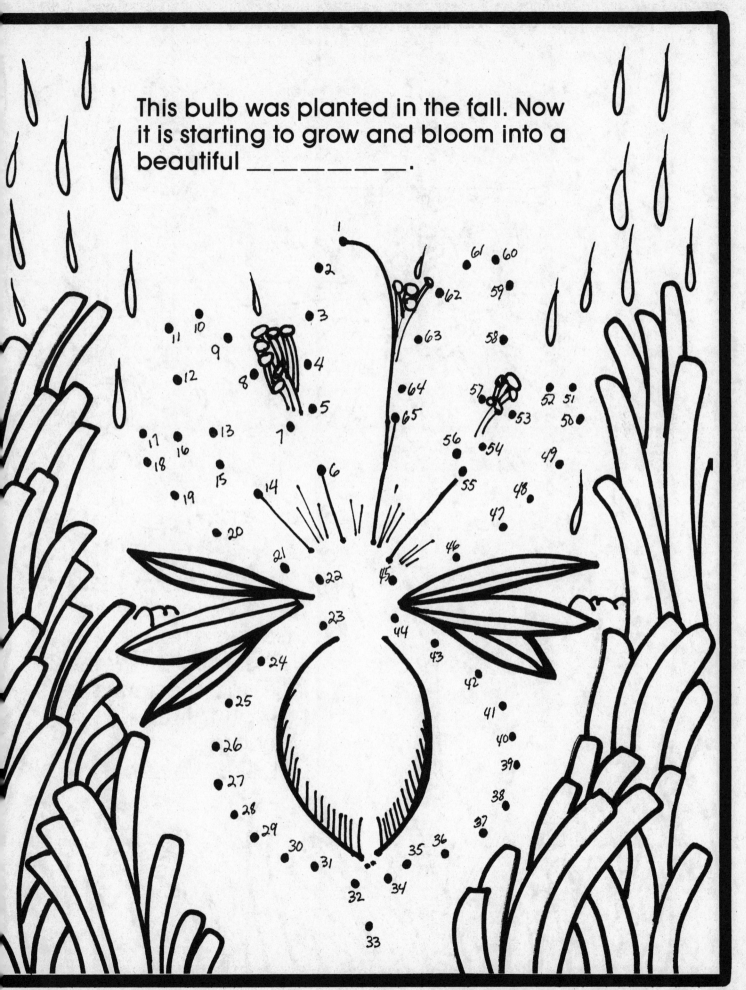

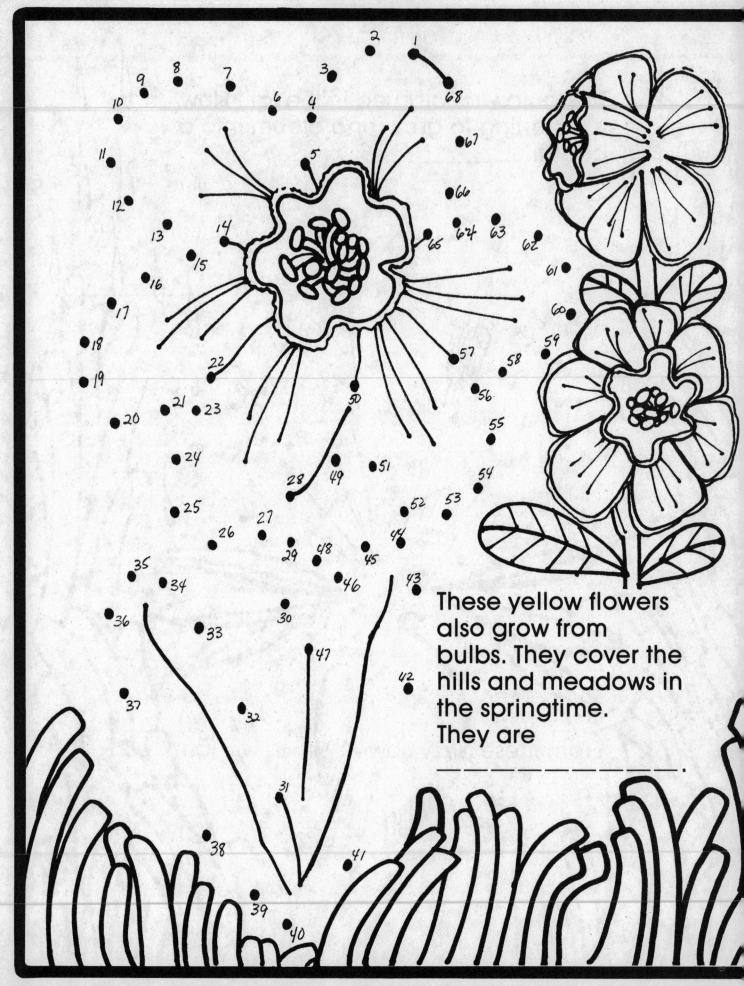

These yellow flowers
also grow from
bulbs. They cover the
hills and meadows in
the springtime.
They are

_____ .

These plants have flowers that are so
soft and furry, they have a kitten's name.
From these fuzzy flowers seeds will form.
This plant is a _____ _____.

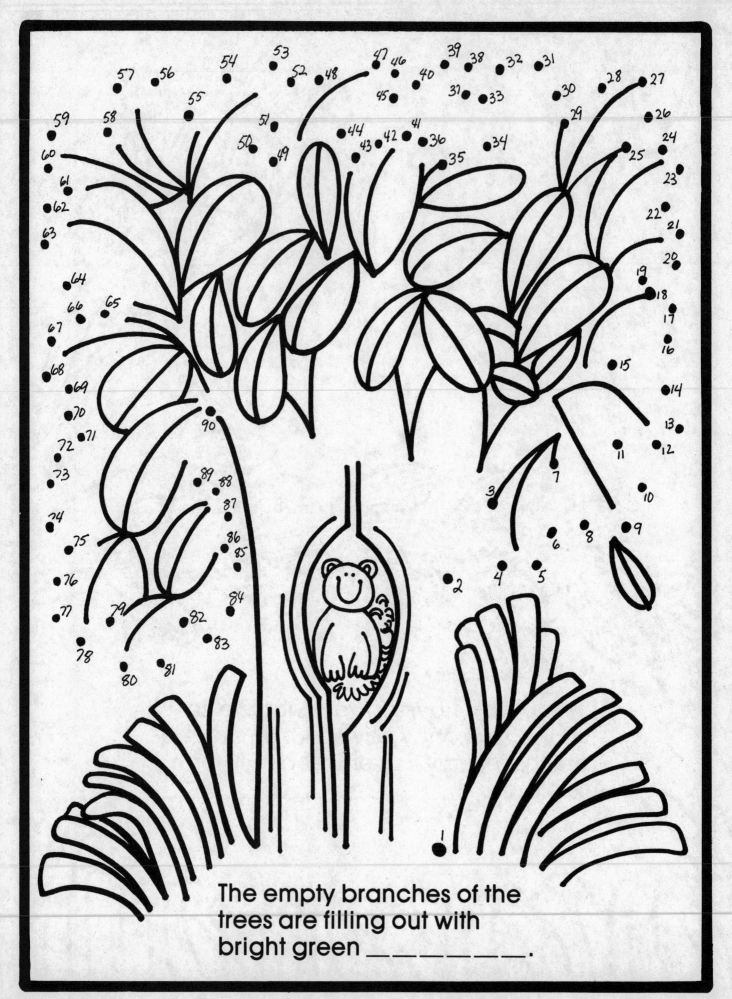

The empty branches of the
trees are filling out with
bright green _ _ _ _ _ _ _ _.

Some trees have pretty flowers in the spring. These are called

_____.

7

New trees are planted in spring. There is a special
day for planting them called _____ Day.

Girls and boys like trees—they're fun to climb. Trees are also the place to build a _ _ _ _ _ _ _ _ _ _.

Spring is the time for Scooter to go to work. He is a

_ _ _ _ _ _ _ _ _ _ .

In the spring, the seeds are planted, and the scarecrow must keep the birds from eating them. The seeds are planted by the farmer as he rides a _____.

It's fun to be on a farm in the spring. Baby animals are born then. A calf is a baby _____.

A lamb is a baby
_ _ _ _ _ _ .

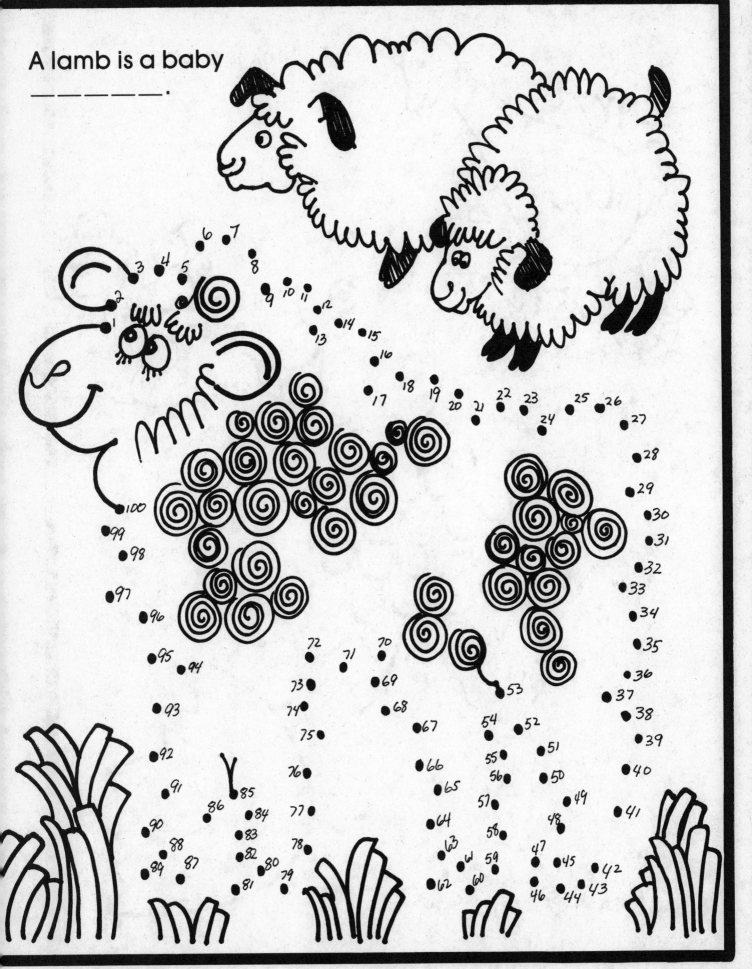

A chick is a baby

_ _ _ _ _ _ _ _ .

14

A piglet is a
baby _____.

This bird is one of the first signs of spring. Color its breast red for it is a _____.

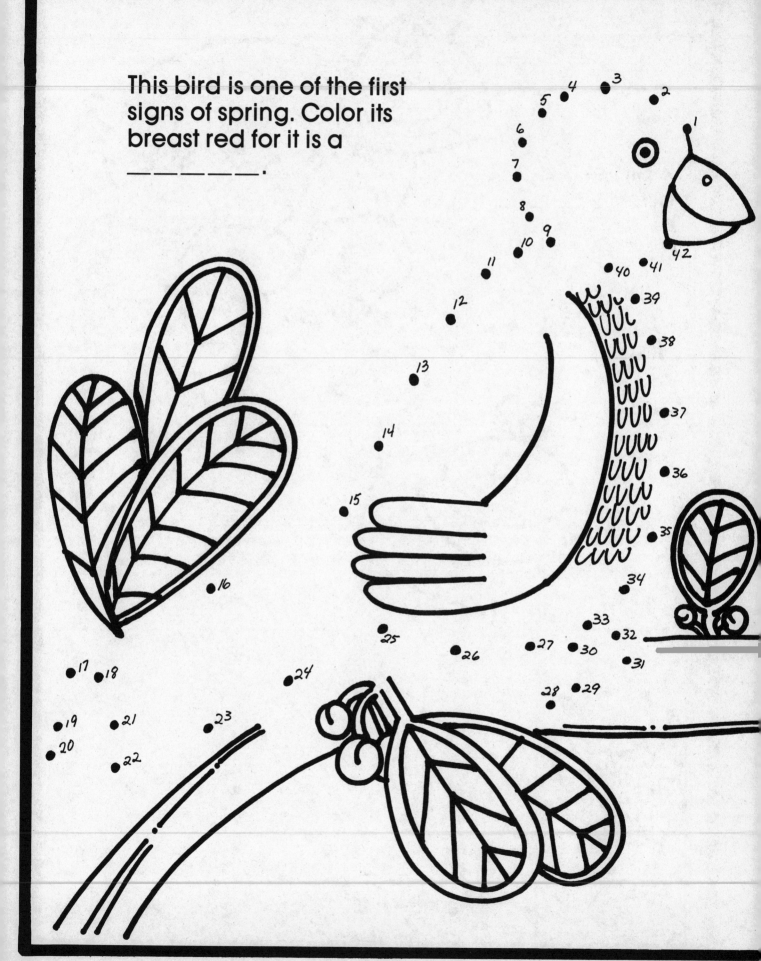

This bird is blue. Its color is part of its name. It is a _____ ____.

The _____ have returned from the warm south, where they spent the winter months.

This bird has pretty red feathers. It is a

_ _ _ _ _ _ _ _ _ _ .

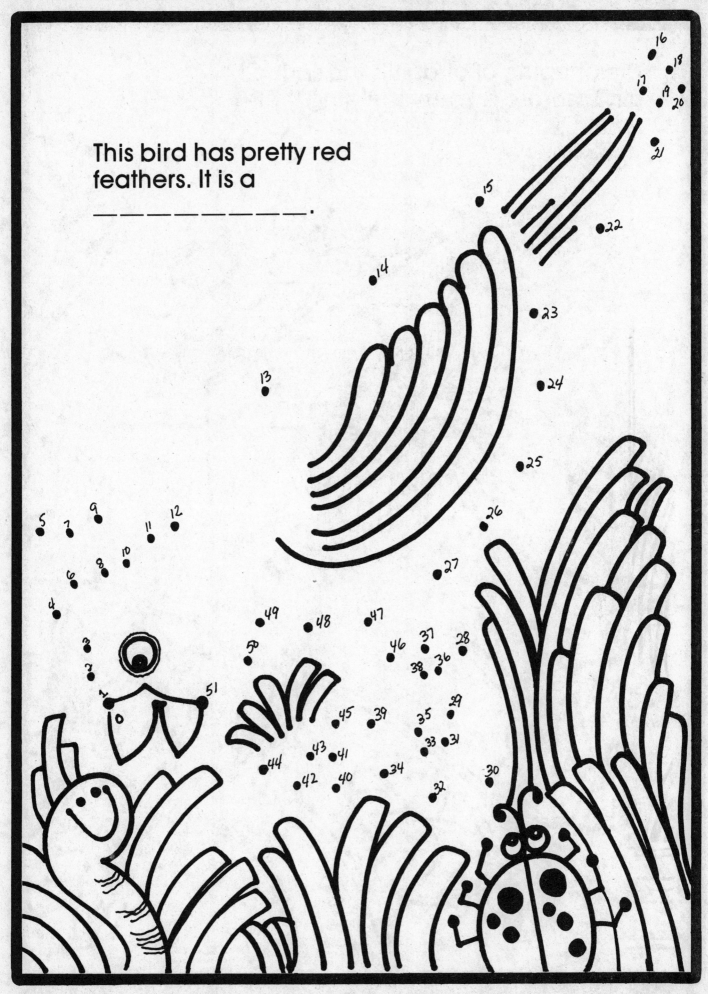

The chirping of birds fills the spring air. They are all busy building their

_ _ _ _ _ _ .

Baby birds will hatch out of
these _____.

Rabbits live in the tall grass of the fields. In the spring, they give birth to many baby _____.

This creature looks something like a worm.
One day it will turn into a beautiful butterfly.
It is a _____.

The nice weather brings great outdoor fun. Jocie is riding her

_____.

Jason is riding his

_ _ _ _ _ _ _ _ .

Spring is the time for this sport. Boys and girls love to play _____.

The weather is so nice,
it's fun to take a
_ _ _ _ _ .

Or you can fly a _ _ _ _ _.

Spring is the time to plant a garden.
This plant creeps along the ground.
From the center of its flower grows a
sweet, red _____ .

These vegetables grow on a vine.
They are found inside a pod.
They are _____.

Answers

2 mushroom
3 flower or crocus
4 daffodils
5 pussy willow
6 leaves
7 blossoms
8 Arbor
9 tree house
10 scarecrow
11 tractor
12 cow
13 sheep
14 chicken
15 pig
16 robin
17 blue jay
18 geese
19 cardinal
20 nests
21 eggs
22 bunnies or rabbits
23 caterpillar
24 bicycle
25 tricycle
26-27 baseball or softball
28 hike
29 kite
30 strawberry
31 peas

Spring is a time for warm weather, new life, and growing. It is a beautiful time of the year.